First published in the UK in 2016 by PICTURA,
an imprint of The Templar Company Limited,
part of the Bonnier Publishing Group,
The Plaza, 535 King's Road,
London, SW10 0SZ
www.templarco.co.uk
www.bonnierpublishing.com

1 3 5 7 9 10 8 6 4 2
0316 008

ISBN 978-1-78370-545-0

Written by Carly Blake
Illustrated by Pedro Correa
Designed by Kieran Hood and Jenny Gabriel

Printed in China

This is just the start.
Pull out your favourite art materials.
Pore over each page.
Think, draw and experiment,
then make this book your own.

Art by Pedro Correa and

....
Write your name here.

PICTURA™

Space Explorer

This is a unique introduction to mankind's exploration of space for aspiring artists and designers. Immerse yourself in inspiring patterns and motifs, fire your imagination with amazing facts and then use your pen to bring these cosmic scenes to life. Every page offers something new to colour, imagine and draw.

Doodle and design.

Stop and start.

Colour and create.

Make your mark.

Customise your stickers

There are two pages of stickers at the back of this book. Give them a spot of colour, then use them to decorate the pages as you like.

Things to look for

Before you put pen to paper, look carefully at all the pages in the book taking in every detail. Can you spot these objects hiding on the pages? Tick the ones that you find.

- ☐ 1 telescope
- ☐ 1 Cassini spacecraft
- ☐ 2 joysticks
- ☐ 4 flags
- ☐ 3 space shuttles

- ☐ 3 rovers
- ☐ 9 footprints
- ☐ 1 floating apple
- ☐ 7 astronauts
- ☐ 3 rockets

Map your own star patterns in the night sky by joining the dots.

Scorpius
(Scorpion)

Ursa Major
(Great Bear)

Sagittarius
(The Archer)

Early stargazers
saw patterns in the
stars. They named
them after mythical
animals, people
or objects.

Earth is not alone in space. Use your brightest pencils to colour all of the planets in the Solar System.

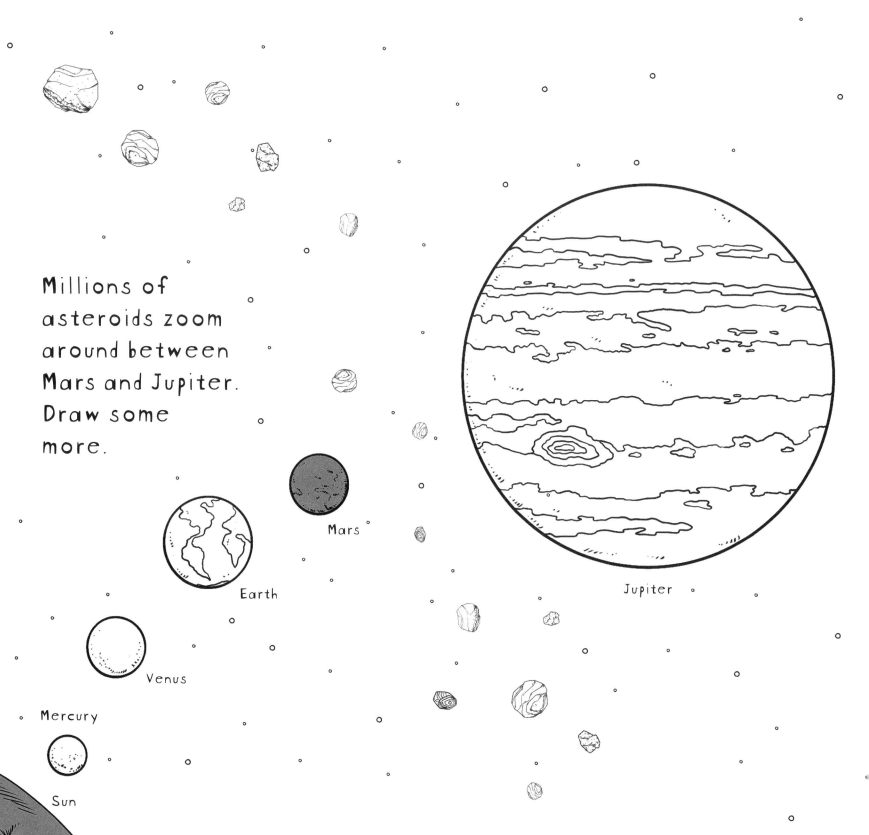

Millions of asteroids zoom around between Mars and Jupiter. Draw some more.

Mars

Earth

Venus

Mercury

Sun

Jupiter

Pluto (dwarf planet)

Neptune

Uranus

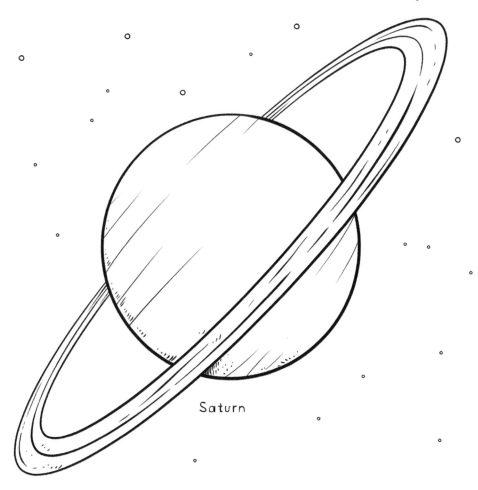

Saturn

Mars, Mercury, Venus, Saturn and Jupiter can be seen from Earth at different times of the year.

The first craft were sent into space in 1957. Design your own out-of-this-world spacecraft!

Sputnik 1 was the first craft in space. It looked like a metal ball with four long legs!

On 20 July, 1969, Neil Armstrong became the first person to walk on the Moon. All around the world people tuned in to watch...

Finish the television picture.

Colour the space mission badges. Create your own cosmic designs for the missions you would like to go on.

This rocket is ready to launch and the engines are blasting into action! Add more billowing clouds of smoke to fill these pages.

Design this rocket.

Colour the countdown.

3... 2... 1...
WE HAVE
LIFT OFF!

The Saturn V rocket, which launched the manned Moon missions, is the most powerful rocket ever built.

Imagine you are an astronaut travelling in a space rocket. Fill the dashboard with colourful dials, switches and buttons.

From launch, it takes 8.5 minutes for a rocket to reach space.

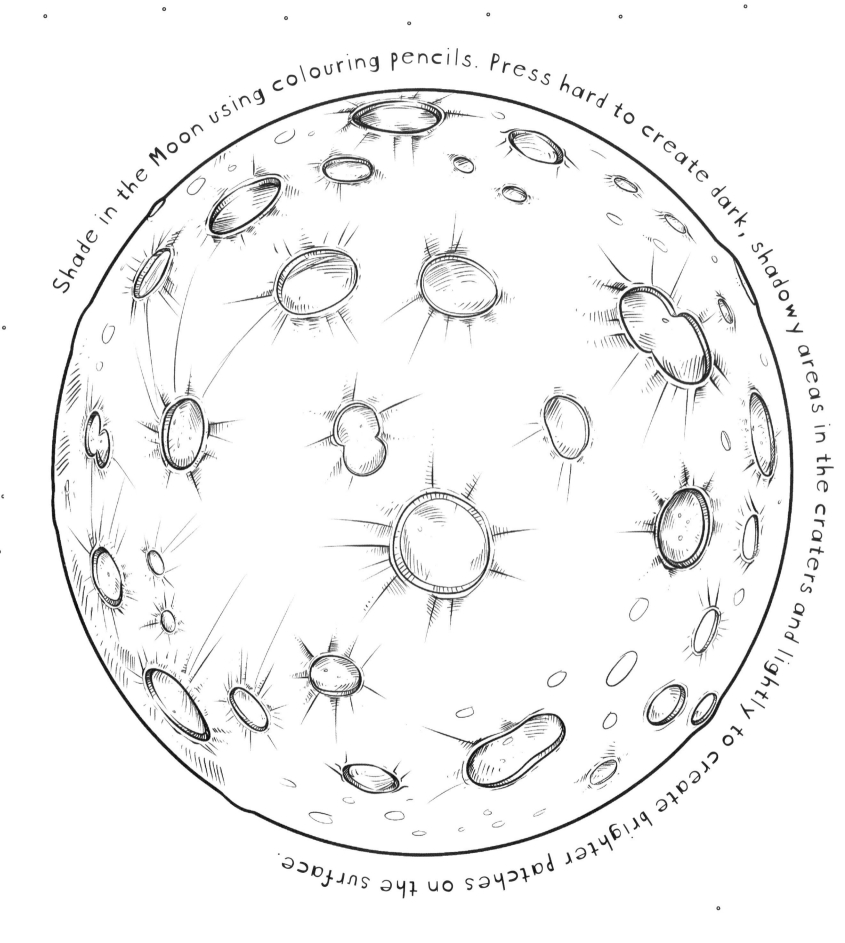

Shade in the Moon using colouring pencils. Press hard to create dark, shadowy areas in the craters and lightly to create brighter patches on the surface.

The side of the Moon that faces away from Earth has hundreds more craters! How many can you draw?

We only ever see one side of the Moon. This is because the Moon rotates as it moves around the Earth.

A robot spacecraft touches down on the surface of the Moon. Create the rocky, rugged landscape it's landing on.

In 1959, Luna 2 became the first spacecraft to land on the Moon.

In 1970 Lunokhod 1 became the first rover to explore the Moon's surface.

Draw the path the rover has travelled from its spacecraft.

Colour the famous scene from 1969 – the first people to walk on the Moon.

Neil Armstrong and Edwin 'Buzz' Aldrin spent 21 hours on the Moon and planted a flag on the surface.

Design your own flag.

Twelve astronauts have walked on the Moon.
Sketch their tracks in the dusty surface.

Add your own footprint on the Moon!

Place your foot on the page and draw around it.

Take a look at the Moon rocks brought back to Earth. Some have layers, some are shiny and some are smooth.

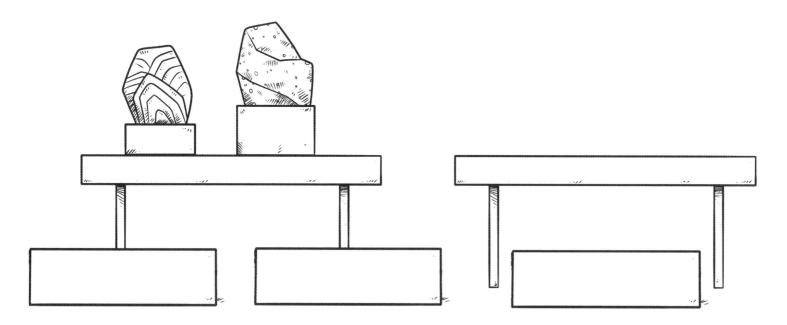

Fill the empty displays with your own extraterrestrial rock drawings. Label what planet they came from.

The largest rock brought back to Earth weighed more than 11 kilograms – the weight of 11 pineapples!

You are standing on the surface of another planet...

You've spotted something on the ground that you want to bring back to Earth...

Draw it.

The view from the Moon looking back at Earth is a spectacular sight! Draw the countries of the world and colour Earth blue and green.

Viewing Earth from the Moon, astronauts described the planet as looking like a 'blue marble'.

Can you see where you live?

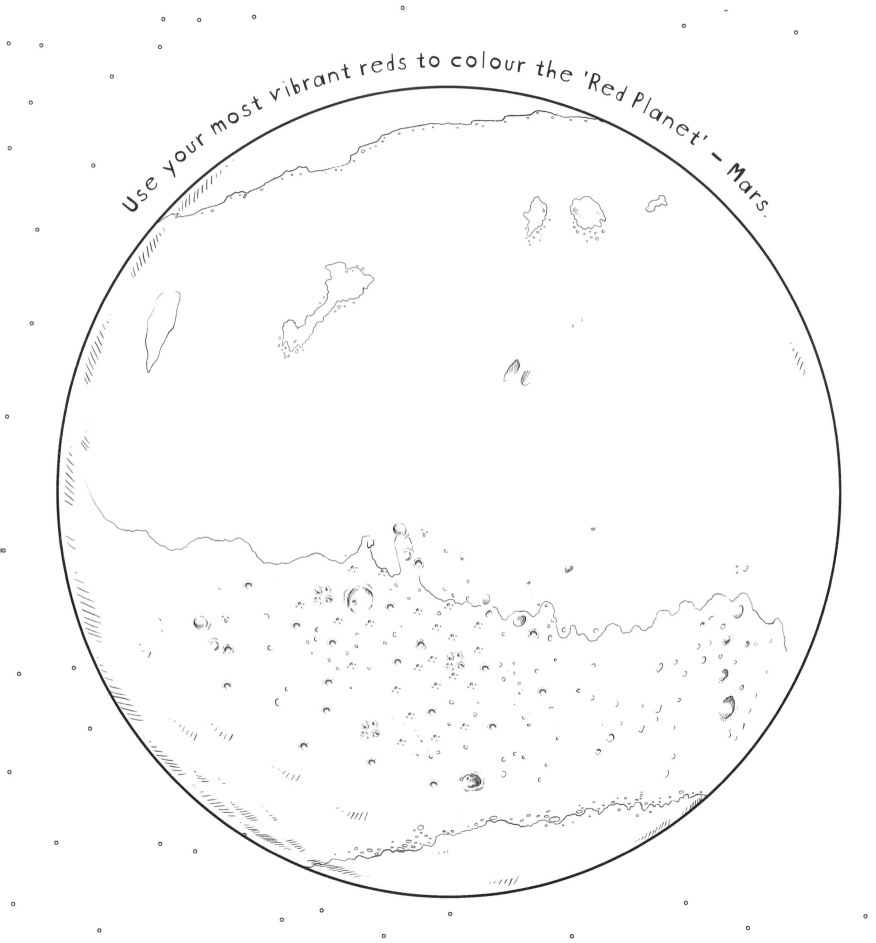

Fill this page with some more spacecraft flying close to Mars.

More missions have been attempted to Mars than any other planet, but only half have been successful.

Equip this high-tech rover with extra gadgets to drill, collect, photograph and measure its findings on the surface of Mars.

The car-sized rover Curiosity began exploring the surface of Mars in 2012. It may discover if life ever existed on Mars.

Curiosity

Four rovers have explored Mars.

What name would you choose for your own rover mission?

Spirit

OPPORTUNITY

CURIOSITY

SOJOURNER

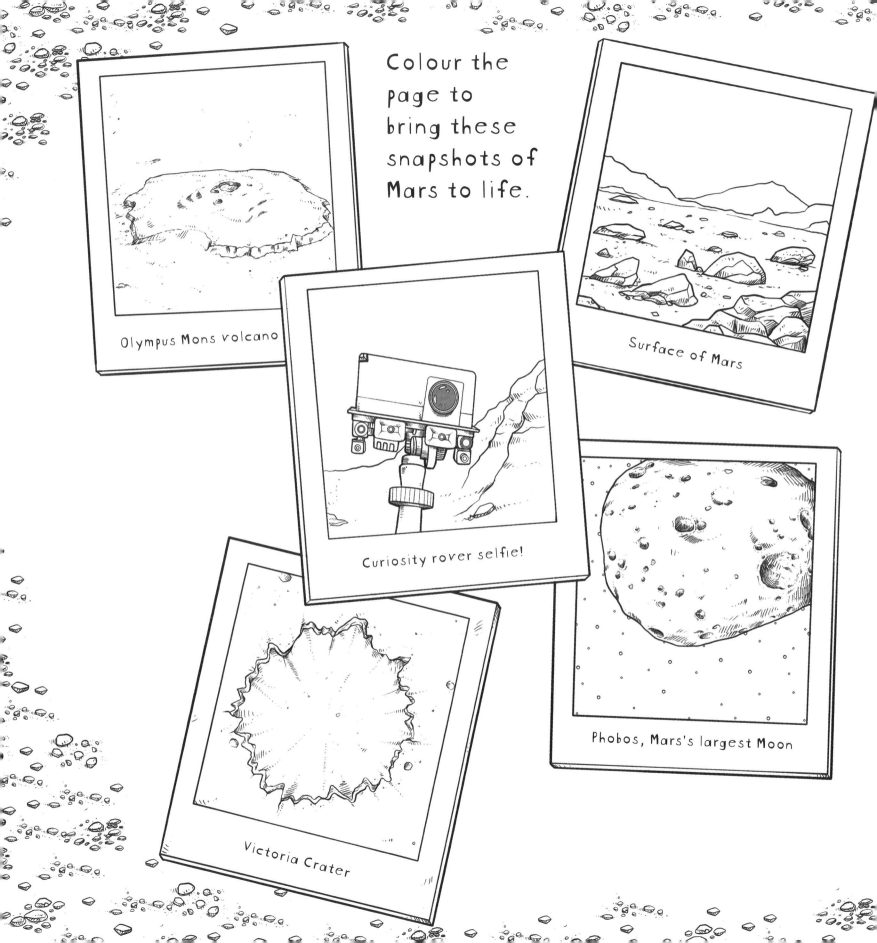

Colour the page to bring these snapshots of Mars to life.

Olympus Mons volcano

Surface of Mars

Curiosity rover selfie!

Phobos, Mars's largest Moon

Victoria Crater

Fill the empty picture frames with your own scenes.

Many spacecraft have sent back fascinating pictures of Mars. One photo shows Olympus Mons – a 25-kilometre-high volcano!

Colour the International Space Station soaring high above the Earth. Use your stickers to add the spacewalking astronauts on the cables.

The International Space Station (ISS) is a huge floating home for astronauts in space! Astronauts 'spacewalk' outside of the ISS to carry out repairs or experiments.

Finish the scene inside the International Space Station. What else is floating around?

What foods are in
these packets and tins?
Draw and colour the
space snacks and write
in the labels.

Design your own space meal.

Watch out for the space debris! Can you find a path through the junk back to the International Space Station? Colour the pages.

More than half a million pieces of space junk are in orbit around Earth. Many are old bits of spacecraft.

Welcome to the Spacecraft Hall of Fame! These long-distance machines have explored beyond Mars.

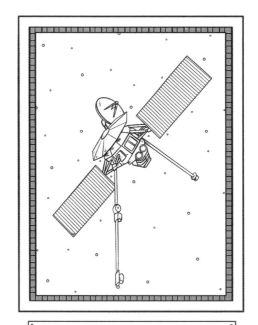

Mariner 10 (arrived 1974)
First spacecraft to visit the smallest planet, Mercury

Pioneer 10 (arrived 1973)
First successful mission to Jupiter

Cassini (arrived 2004)
Carrying out in-depth study of Saturn, its rings and moons

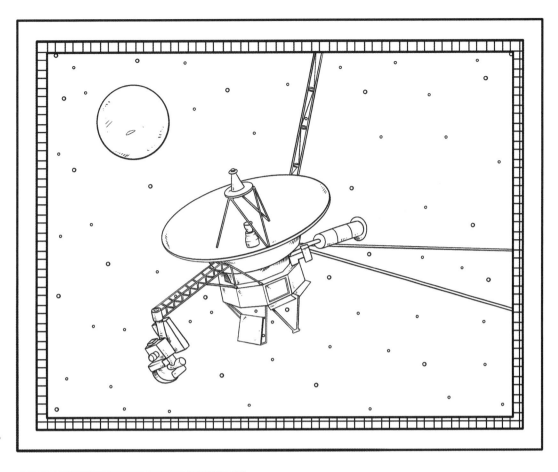

Voyager 2 (1986–1989)
Only spacecraft to orbit
Uranus and Neptune

Venus Express
(arrived 2006)
Spacecraft began a
long-term study of Venus

New Horizons
(arrived 2015)
Only spacecraft to
explore Pluto

After exploring
Uranus and Neptune,
Voyager 2 travelled
away from Earth. It is
still sending back data
from the edge of the
Solar System.

Design a spacesuit that could protect against the extreme heat and cold on Mercury, the closest planet to the Sun.

On Mercury it can be as hot as 400°C and as cold as -170°C! (Temperatures on Earth range from 58°C to -89°C.)

Craters of all shapes and sizes cover Mercury's surface.
Use a rainbow of colour to fill them in.

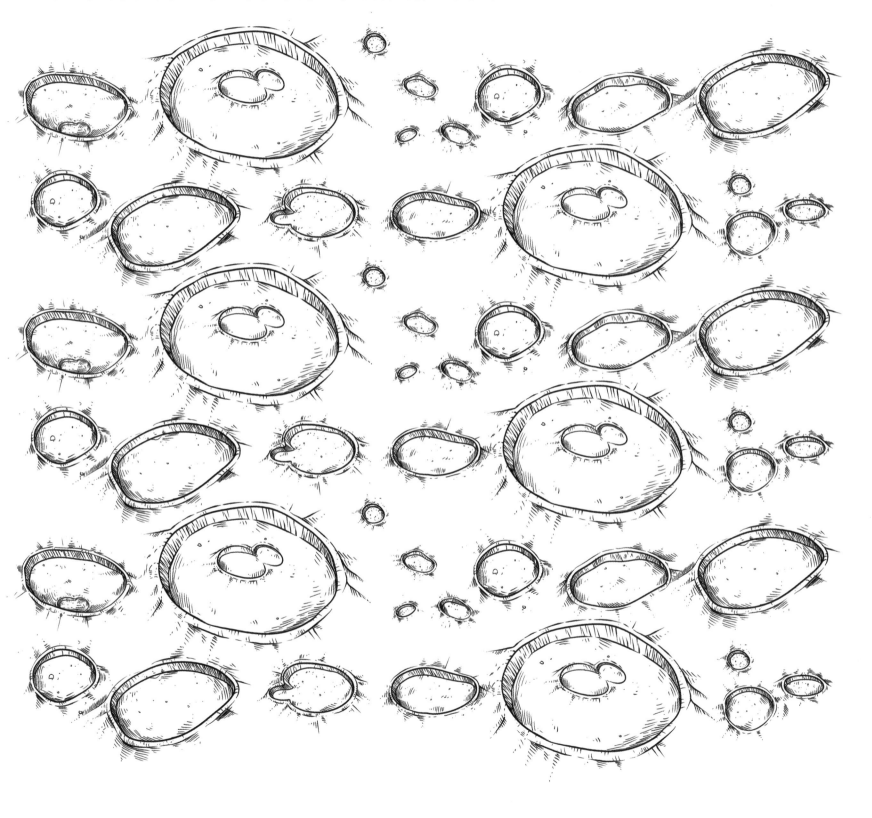

Make the craters on fiery planet Venus erupt with lava and flames.

More than 30 spacecraft have visited Venus. Several landed on the surface but didn't survive for long in the harsh conditions.

Jupiter is bigger than all of the other planets in the Solar System added together. Colour this jumbo planet's brown, red and yellow bands and add its Great Red Spot.

Great Red Spot

Spacecraft have captured close-up pictures of Jupiter's Great Red Spot – a huge storm that has raged for hundreds of years.

Add Saturn's beautiful swirling rings

stretching out around the planet.

Spacecraft that studied Saturn discovered its rings are made up of bits of ice, dust and rock — some as small as sand grains, others as big as buildings!

Can you imagine an alien life form that might survive in the icy-cold atmosphere of Uranus? Draw it amongst the hazy blue-green clouds.

Uranus, the coldest planet in the Solar System, was only discovered in **1781**. Just one spacecraft has visited this distant icy world.

Colour Neptune shades of brilliant blue. Surround the planet with 14 moons – one of them is shaped like an egg!

Voyager 2 arrived at Neptune in 1989 and sent back pictures of this dazzling planet. The gases in Neptune's atmosphere make it appear bright blue.

Use your brightest yellows, reds and oranges to colour the Sun.

Spacecraft designed to fly close to the Sun are equipped with thick heat shields to survive the blazing temperatures.

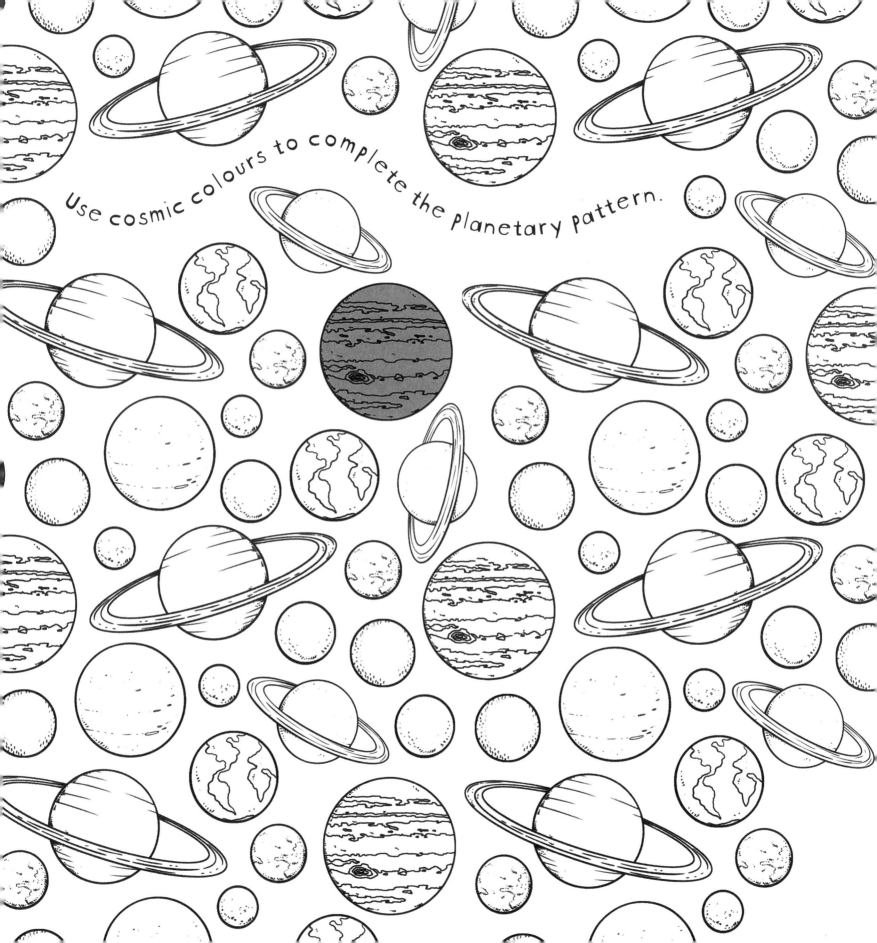

Use cosmic colours to complete the planetary pattern.

A comet is a huge ball of ice and dust with a glowing tail. They come from the very outer zones of the Solar System.

Design your own certificate from the Astronaut Academy.
Write in your name and where you would like to explore!

Name: ....

Has completed their astronaut training and is certified to go into space.

Date certificate issued:

....

First mission departure date: ....

To explore: ....

Signed: ....

(Jimmy Galactic, Director of the Astronaut Academy)